Spell with Zip

Zip

Zip is a friendly space alien from planet Zee. He loves to learn. Zip uses his hands to speak to his friends. He can't wait to teach the people of planet Earth all about sign language. Zip is the captain of his spaceship.

Pella

Pella is Zip's best friend. She also comes from planet Zee. Pella is very brave. Although she is a little younger than Zip and Statz, she isn't afraid of anything and is always the first of the three friends to try new things.

Statz

Statz is in charge of computers on the spaceship. He loves gadgets. Statz uses his Zablet to help him and his friends out of sticky situations. He is excited to learn about planet Earth and all the people who live here.

Goober

Goober is an unexpected guest on the friends' adventures. A greedy and naughty space stowaway, Goober has the ability to change his colour and shape so is always jumping out and surprising Zip, Pella and Statz.

Zip's top tips

Zip and friends are here to help you talk in a fun new way - spell with your fingers and talk with your hands. Follow these top tips to get the most from their adventures:

- **Share the book together and enjoy the story**
- **Play with the signs**
- **Use Zip's alphabet to make your own words**
- **Visit Space School, enjoy the activities and have fun**
- **Watch out for Goober...**

SignSpell

Zip and the Journey to Earth

Travelling very quickly through the vast darkness of space is a bright green spaceship.

On board are three alien explorers searching for new adventures on distant planets. The three aliens are the best of friends. The captain's name is Zip and his friends are Pella and Statz.

They love watching the stars and planets whizz by.

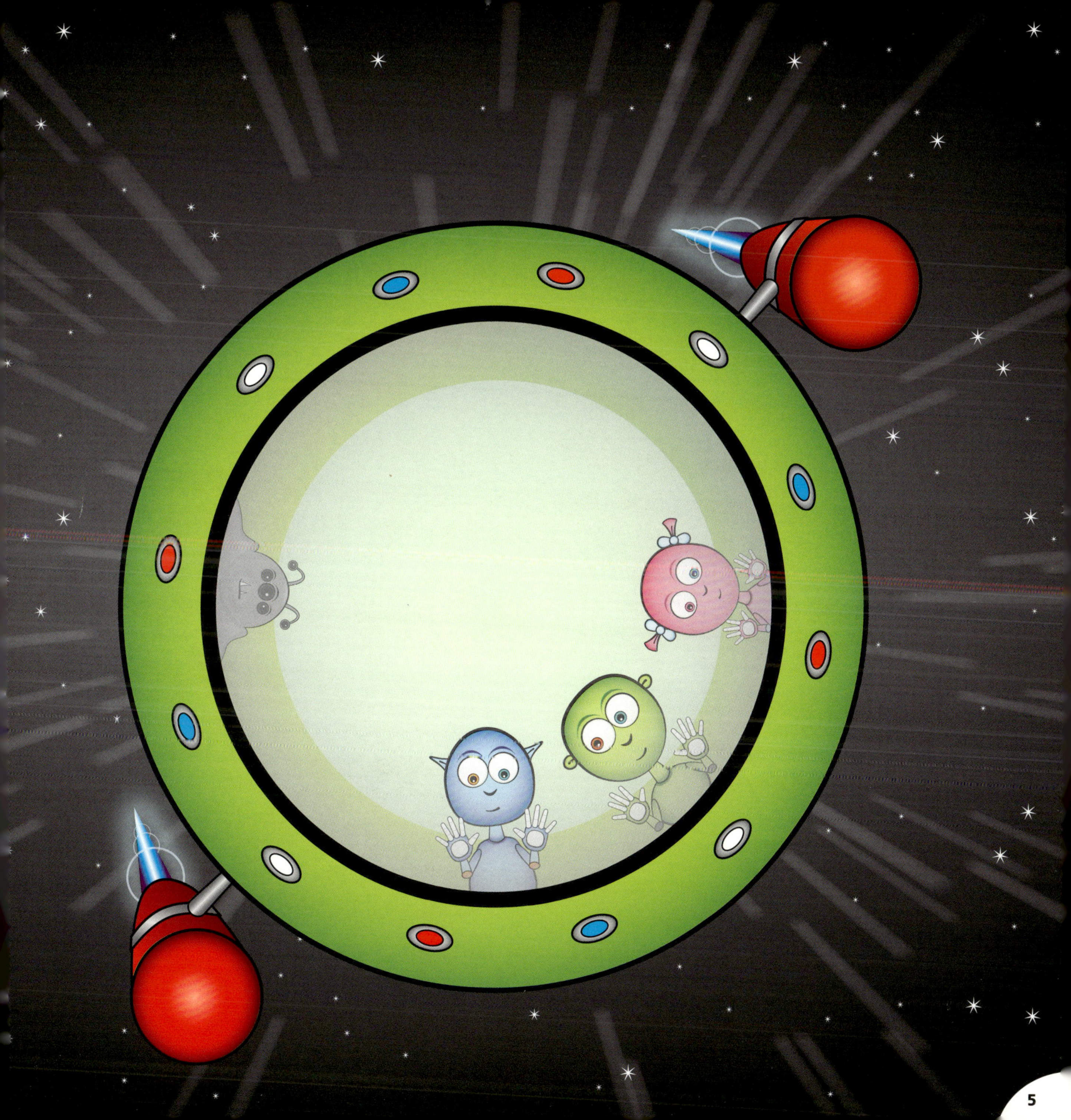

Zip checks the control panel and notices the spaceship is running low on power.

“We need to recharge the ship,” he tells his friends. “Statz, can you find out if there are any energy sources near here, please?”

“There's a bright star called the Sun quite close,” says Statz, checking his Zablet. “We will be able to charge up using its solar power.”

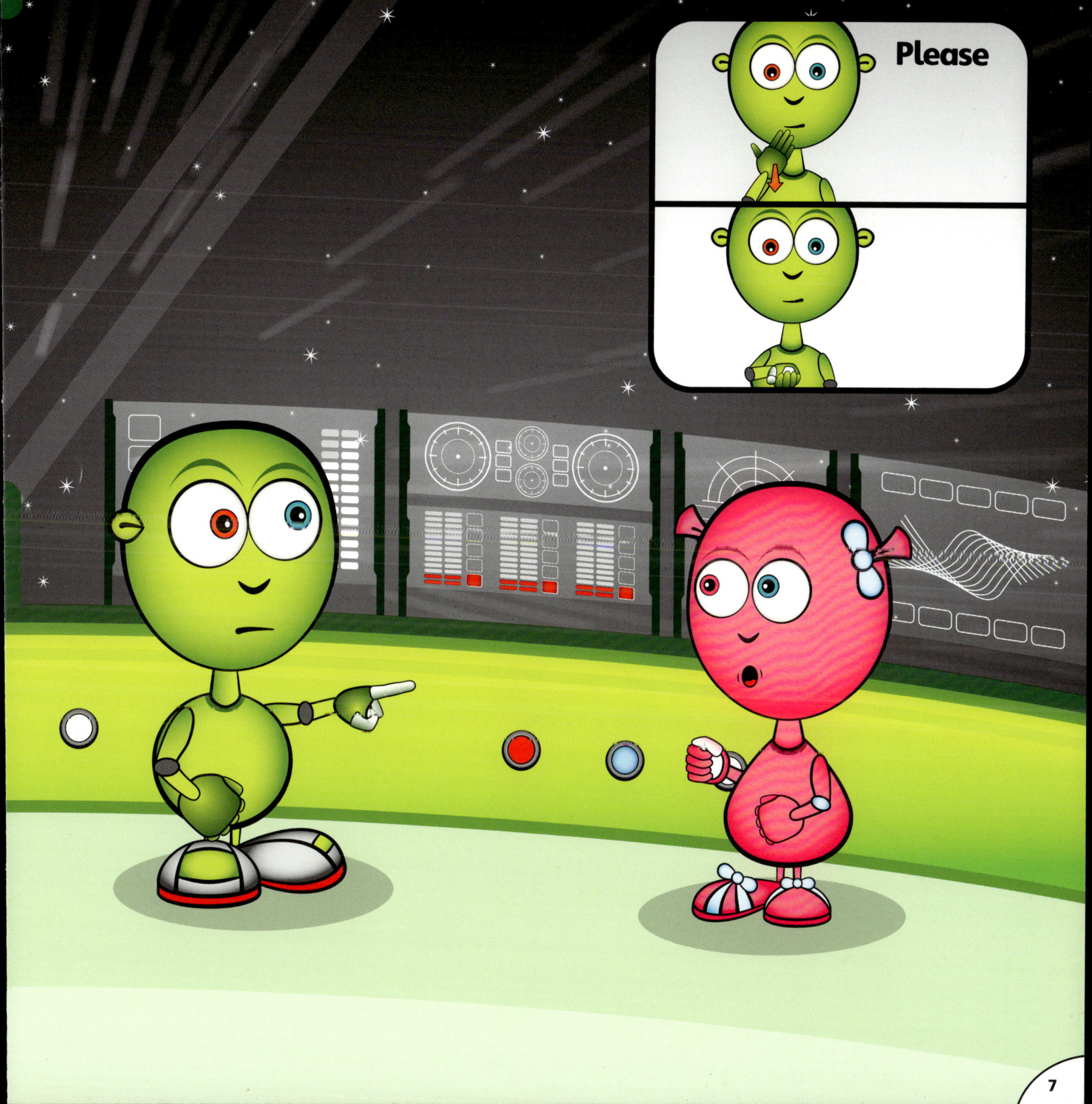
Please

Zip steers the spaceship towards the sun.

On their way they pass some planets.

Pella has her nose pressed to the window.
"That planet has rings around it," she says. "It's beautiful."

Statz looks at the star map on his Zablet.
"It's called Saturn, Pella. It spins very quickly."

Zip spots another planet. “That is definitely my favourite so far,” he tells his friends, “it’s very red.”

“It’s called Mars,” says Statz. “It’s a very rocky planet with no reported life forms.”

“Thank you, Statz,” says Zip.

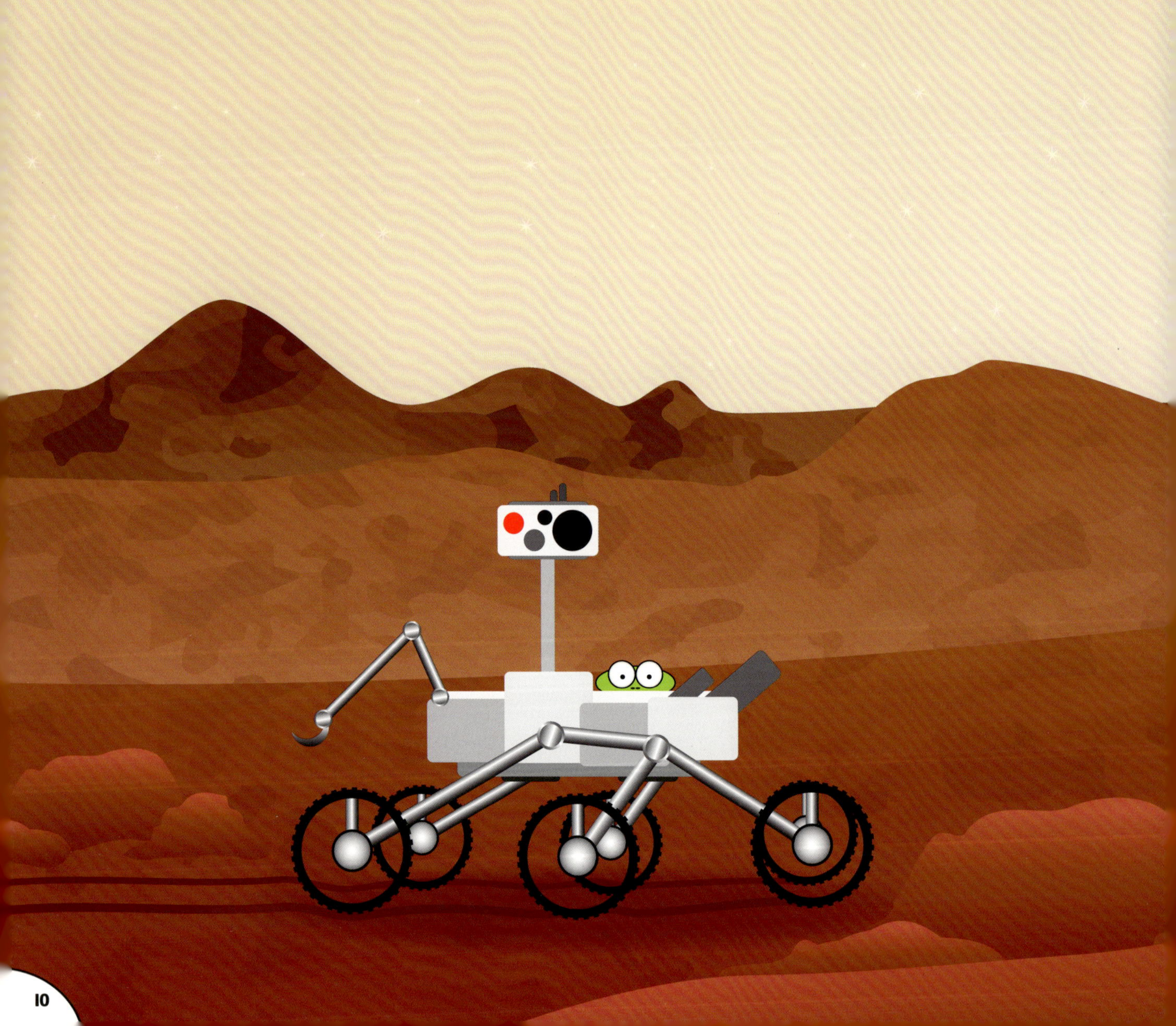

Thank You

Meet

Zip slows the spaceship as it approaches the sun. While the ship recharges, Pella and Statz look at the planets around them.

"Is there any life on those planets?" Pella asks Statz.

"Lots of humans live on that blue and green one over there," he tells her.

Pella would really like to visit that planet. "Can we go there to meet them?" she asks.

Zip points the spaceship towards planet Earth.

Pella checks the control panel. “It’s going to get very hot as we enter Earth’s atmosphere,” she tells her friends.

“I’m sorry if we have a bumpy landing,” says Zip. “We’re going very fast!”

Space School

Zip is showing you the signs you have learnt in the story so far.
Can you remember what they are?
See if you can spell each one using Zip's alphabet.

The friends hit the planet's surface with a splash not a bump.

The spaceship has landed in the sea and drifts slowly to the sea bed.

The water fizzes as the spaceship cools down.

"That was a good landing, Zip. Well done," says Pella.

Zip gets ready to explore in his space helmet and flippers, but his friends think that is a bad idea.

Statz looks at his friends. "If we want to meet humans, we will have to find some land to explore."

Good
Bad

The spaceship takes off again and bursts out of the water.

The friends wave goodbye to the sea and head towards the shore.

The spaceship lands on dry land. The friends can't wait to explore planet Earth and make some human friends.

"Let's get ready," says Pella.

Zip, Pella and Statz go straight to the sleeping pod to get Zip's backpack and anything else they can find to help them explore planet Earth. The friends search high and low but they can't find any of their things.

Space School

Zip can't wait to explore planet Earth.
Can you remember the signs Zip will use when he meets humans?

The friends go from room to room, but still can't find their things.

"It's just like when that naughty creature hid all our stuff back on planet Zee," says Zip. "You don't think we brought him with us, do you?"

Pella sees something move in the darkness. "Hello," she says. "Is there anybody there?"

Oh no! It is him...

GOOBER!

Zip's Signs

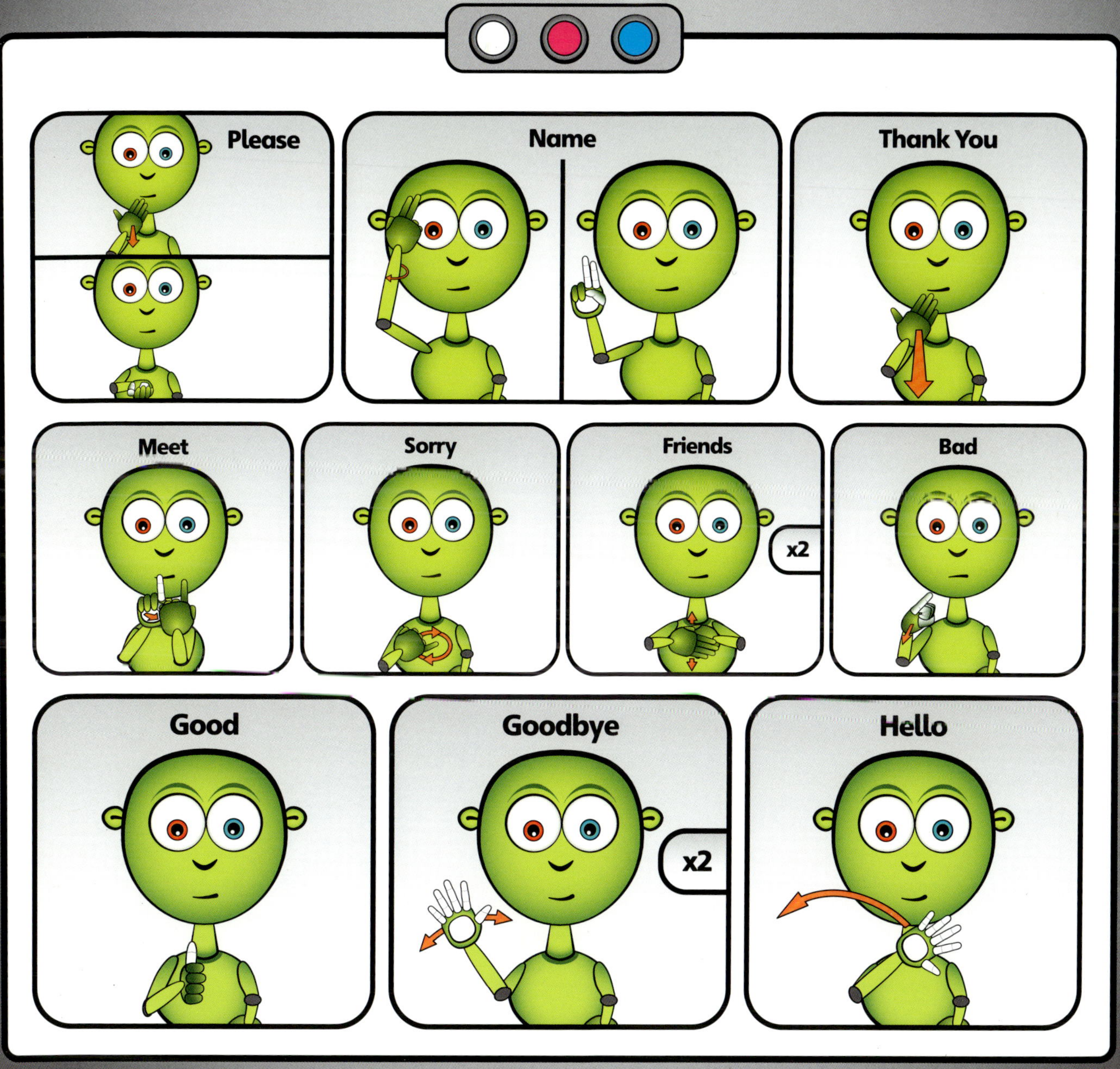
Please
Name
Thank You
Meet
Sorry
Friends
x2
Bad
Good
Goodbye
x2
Hello

Fun things to do

Now that you have read all about Zip and the Journey to Earth, here are some fun things for you to do:

- **What do you think aliens on planet Mars would look like? Describe, draw or make**
- **Make up a new planet. What shape would it be?**
- **How would you feel if you had been away from planet Earth for a long time?**
- **If you landed on a new planet, where would you explore first?**
- **What would you do if you found Goober in your bedroom?**
- **Teach a friend to spell their name using Zip's alphabet**

First published 2013 by Signature

SignSpell® stories created by Signature
Designed and illustrated by Igloo Imaging Ltd.